USBORNE VERY FIRST READ

Phonics Workbook 1

s a t p i n m d

Written by Mairi Mackinnon

Illustrated by Fred Blunt

Designed by Caroline Spatz

Reading and handwriting consultants:

Alison Kelly and Anne Washtell, Roehampton University

S

Find the big **S** on the sticker pages and stick it here.

Say the sound: sssss
Write a big **S** in the air.
Write **S** with your finger on the table.

Colour in all the things below that begin with **S**.
Put blue **S** stickers next to those pictures.

Did you colour in sun, sock and scissors?
Give yourself a star from the sticker pages.

WELL DONE!

Hungry frogs

Give each frog a long curly tongue so it can catch a bug for its supper.
Start at the bug and follow the curves into the frog's mouth.
You can draw more bubbles and frogspawn in the pond, too.

Trace the **S** with your pencil and write some more. Start at the dot:

S S S .

Sam the chef needs to hang up his saucepans.
Draw some **S**-shaped hooks for him. Then choose some pans from the sticker pages
and hang them on the hooks.

What is Sam making for supper? Is it sausages, soup, sardines or sauce?
Can you draw it in his pan?

Find the big **a** on the sticker pages and stick it here.

Say the sound: a-a-a-
Write a big **a** in the air.
Write **a** with your finger on the table.

Colour in all the things below that begin with **a**.
Put red **a** stickers next to those pictures.

Did you colour in apple, ambulance and anchor?
Give yourself a star from the sticker pages.

WELL DONE!

Apples and ants

Finish drawing around the apple shapes below.
Start from the dots just under the stalks. Then you can choose
some ants from the sticker pages and add them to the picture.

Trace the **a** with your pencil and write some more:

a a a a a

It's time for the school photograph at Additup Academy.
The boys are standing at the back, the girls are sitting down in front.
Finish the girls' faces with **a** shapes.

Adam, Alice, Akram, Amina...
Can you think of any more names beginning with **a**?

nd the big **t** on the sticker pages and stick it here.

the sound: t-t-t-

ite a big **t** in the air.

te **t** with your finger on the table.

ur in all the things below that begin with **t**.

yellow **t** stickers next to those pictures.

Did you colour in tiger, teapot and tent?
Give yourself a star from the sticker pages.

WELL DONE!

Teddies in the rain

Terrible weather today! Draw some umbrella handles so these teddies can hold up their umbrellas and not get wet. You can colour in the umbrellas, too.

Trace the **t** with your pencil and write some more:

t

These ships need anchors! Finish the anchors with **t** shapes, then choose turtles from the sticker pages to stick in the water around them.

p

Find the big **p** on the sticker pages and stick it here.

Say the sound: p-p-p-
Write a big **p** in the air.
Write **p** with your finger on the table.

Colour in all the things below that begin with **p**.
Put pink **p** stickers next to those pictures.

Did you colour in pirate, pencil, pear and pumpkin?
Give yourself a star from the sticker pages.

WELL DONE!

Penguins in the park

These penguins are having fun! Can you find:

- a penguin family having a picnic
- baby penguins paddling in the pool
- two penguins playing ping-pong
- a penguin playing the piano
- a penguin painting a picture
- a penguin in a parachute?

When you have found them,
put orange (P) stickers next to them.

Can you spot any more
things beginning with **p**?

Trace the **p** with your pencil and write some more:

p p p p pp ppp p

Poppy and Patrick are in the parrot house at the zoo. Finish drawing around the parrots' bodies and tails using **p** shapes. Then choose some flying parrots and parakeets from the sticker pages, and add them to the picture.

Making words

Put **s** - **a** - **t** together and you get **sat**.
Read the letters, then read the word, then write it.

s a t sat sat

What do you get if you put **p** - **a** - **t** together?
Read the letters, then read the word, then write it.

p a t pat pat

How about **t** - **a** - **p**?

t a p tap tap

Which of these pictures is right for sat? Write **sat** underneath:

1   2   3

Which of these pictures is right for pat? Write **pat** underneath:

4

5

6

....

Which of these pictures is right for tap? Write **tap** underneath:

7

8

9

....

Did you write **sat** for picture 3, **pat** for picture 5 and **tap** for picture 7?
Give yourself a star from the sticker pages.

WELL
DONE!

Find the big **i** on the sticker pages and stick it here.

Say the sound: i-i-i-
Write a big **i** in the air.
Write **i** with your finger on the table.

Colour in all the things below that begin with **i**.
Put orange **i** stickers next to those pictures.

Did you colour in igloo and ink?
Give yourself a star from the sticker pages.

WELL DONE!

m m m m
m m m

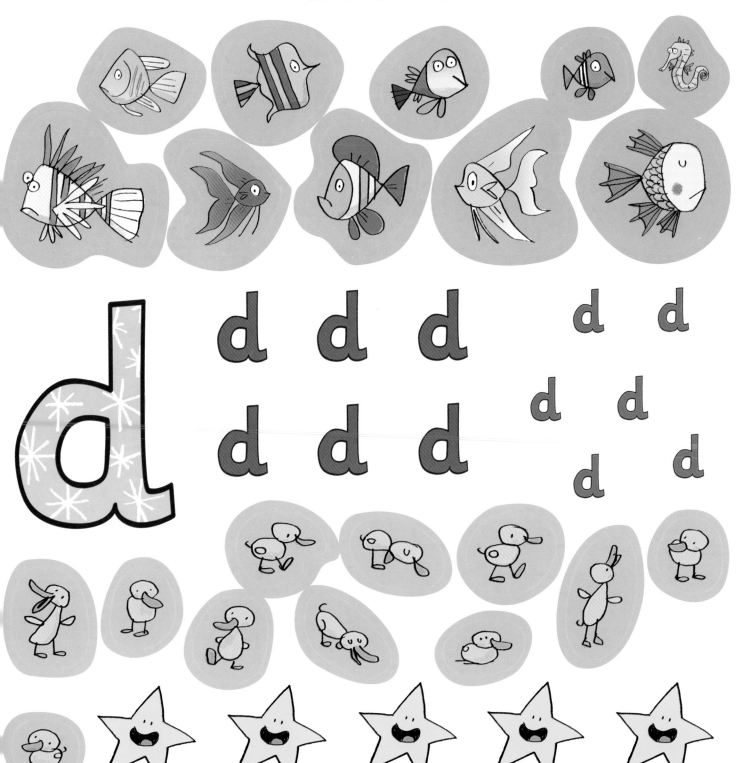

d d d d d d

d d d d d d

d d

Incomplete insects

All insects should have six legs - but some of the ones below don't!
Can you finish them off so that each insect has enough?

Trace the **i** with your pencil and write some more.
Start with the lines, then add the dots.

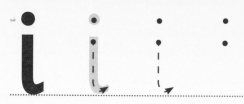

Isabelle and Imran both have their birthday today. Can you finish drawing the candles on their birthday cakes using **i** shapes? Then choose some presents from the sticker pages and stick them on the table.

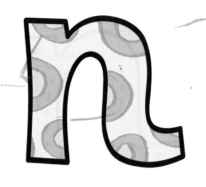

Find the big **n** on the sticker pages and stick it here.

Say the sound: nnnnn

Write a big **n** in the air.

Write **n** with your finger on the table.

Colour in all the things below that begin with **n**.
Put green **n** stickers next to those pictures.

Did you colour in nest, nail, nurse and net?
Give yourself a star from the sticker pages.

WELL DONE!

N-N-N-Nessie!

This fisherman needn't be nervous - the three beasties are quite friendly. Draw around their humps, starting at the dots.

Trace the **n** with your pencil and write some more:

These nine fine elephants are out on parade.
Finish their heads with **n** shapes, then choose some
baby elephant stickers from the sticker pages.

Making words

Put **s - i - p** together and you get **sip**.
Read the letters, then read the word, then write it.

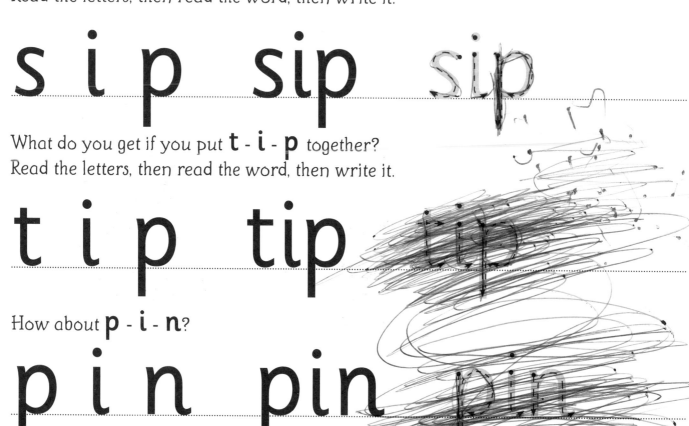

s i p sip sip

What do you get if you put **t - i - p** together?
Read the letters, then read the word, then write it.

t i p tip

How about **p - i - n**?

p i n pin

Which of these pictures is right for sip? Write **sip** underneath:

1

2

3

Which of these pictures is right for tip? Write **tip** underneath:

4   5   6

....

Which of these pictures is right for pin? Write **pin** underneath:

7   8   9

....

WELL
DONE!

Find the big **m** on the sticker pages and stick it here.

Say the sound: mmmm
Write a big **m** in the air.
Write **m** with your finger on the table.

Colour in all the things below that begin with **m**.
Put purple **m** stickers next to those pictures.

Did you colour in moon, monkey, mushroom and mouse?
Give yourself a star from the sticker pages.

WELL DONE!

Munch munch

These mice need to reach the cheese quickly!
Draw around their ears so that they can hear
if Max the marmalade cat wakes up,
and scurry away to safety.

Trace the **m** with your pencil and write some more:

m   m   m   m

Molly, Minna and Marlon have gone diving. Can you finish their masks using **m** shapes? Then add some tropical fish from the sticker pages. And - the divers haven't noticed, but could that be a mermaid below them?

Find the big **d** on the sticker pages and stick it here.

Say the sound: d-d-d-
Write a big **d** in the air.
Write **d** with your finger on the table.

Colour in all the things below that begin with **d**.
Put blue **d** stickers next to those pictures.

Did you colour in doll, duck, donkey and dog?
Give yourself a star from the sticker pages.

WELL DONE!

Dinosaurs galore

These dinos are doing all kinds of different things.
Can you spot:

- two dinosaurs dancing
- a dinosaur diving into the deep blue sea
- three dinosaurs having a delicious dinner
- a dinosaur dentist
- a dinosaur detective making a discovery?

When you have found them,
put red **d** stickers next to them.

Can you spot any more things
beginning with **d**?

Trace the **d** with your pencil and write some more:

Daisy, David and Daniel are feeding bread to the ducks. Can you finish the ducks' bodies using **d** shapes? Then choose some little ducklings from the sticker pages.

Making words

Put **m - a - t** together and you get **mat**.
Read the letters, then read the word, then write it.

m a t   mat   *mat*

What do you get if you put **m - a - n** together?
Read the letters, then read the word, then write it.

m a n   man   *man*

How about **s - a - d**?

s a d   sad   *sad*

Which of these pictures is right for mat? Write **mat** underneath:

1

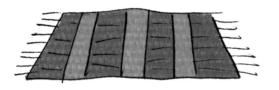

2

3

....

Which of these pictures is right for man? Write **man** underneath:

4   5   6

....

Which of these pictures is right for sad? Write **sad** underneath:

7   8   9

....

Did you write **mat** for picture 1, **man** for picture 6 and **sad** for picture 8?
Give yourself a star from the sticker pages.

WELL DONE!

Capital letters

You use capital letters at the beginning of a name or a sentence.
Trace and then copy the pairs of capital letters and small letters below.
Start with the dotted line.

WELL DONE!

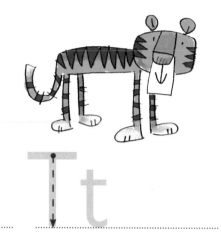

Ss   Aa   Tt

Pp   Ii   Nn

Mm   Dd

Edited by Lesley Sims and Jenny Tyler

First published in 2011 by Usborne Publishing Ltd., Usborne House, 83-85 Saffron Hill, London EC1N 8RT, England. www.usborne.com
Copyright © 2011 Usborne Publishing Ltd.